To SpongeBob's #1 Fan:

You are holding in your hands the first-EVER collection of SpongeBob comics. Pretty cool, huh? Some of these comics are more than ten years old, while some are brand-spanking-new. But all of these comics were created for *Nick Magazine*, mostly by the same artists who write and draw so many of the *SpongeBob* episodes you know and love.

That's where I come in. My name is Sherm Cohen, and I'm one of the *SpongeBob SquarePants* storyboard artists who worked on these comic stories. Now, some of you might be wondering, "What's a storyboard artist?" Well, a storyboard artist sketches the pictures for a *SpongeBob* cartoon, the first step in bringing a cartoon to life.

A comic is sort of like a storyboard before it gets animated for TV, except that a comic has word balloons, captions, sound effects, and tons of color! Storyboard artists can have loads of fun with comics because comics don't follow the same strict guidelines as TV. We can shake things up by using big panels and little panels. We can make a comic into a four-panel-long joke, or a ten-page adventure epic. And we can use all kinds of drawing styles—everything from the classic version of our favorite talking sponge to superfunky styles that make Bikini Bottom look crazy!

This collection combines comics of all shapes, sizes, lengths, and art styles . . . all brought to you by a bunch of cartoonists who love to tell funny stories.

These comics began life the same way a TV cartoon does: A handful of cartoonists sit around a table and toss ideas around until we find one that's full of funny possibilities and cool things to draw. For example, what would happen if SpongeBob got the hiccups and just couldn't stop? That little idea began to turn into an epic adventure when SpongeBob's creator, Stephen Hillenburg, suggested that Mr. Krabs might banish SpongeBob to a mythical place called Hiccup Island! My pal Derek Drymon suggested a journey to a spooky island haunted by the Flying Dutchman! I couldn't wait to get home and start sketching out the story while those images were flying around inside my head.

I had a great time drawing that story, and I'm really glad you'll have a chance to read that tale here, along with the rest of the best of the SpongeBob comic stories.

Enjoy!

Sherm Cohen
Storyboard Artist (one of many!)
and Storyboard Supervisor
for *SpongeBob SquarePants* (Seasons 1-4)

Comic Crazy!

DIRECTLY FROM THE PAGES OF

Nick magazine

SCHOLASTIC INC.

New York Toronto London Auckland Sydney

Mexico City New Delhi Hong Kong Buenos Aires

"Prize Inside": Story, art, and lettering by Graham Annable. Coloring by Sno Cone Studios. "Hiccup! And Away!": Plot: Paul Tibbet. Script, art, and lettering: Sherm Cohen. Coloring: Digital Chameleon. Special thanks to: Stephen Hillenburg and Derek Drymon. "Just Desserts": Story, art, and lettering: C.H. Greenblatt. Coloring: Sno Cone Studios. "Krusty Krab Cleanup": Story: Paul Tibbit. Pencils: Mark O'Hare. Inks: Sherm Cohen. Coloring: Nick Jennings. "Dollars and Scents": Story, art, and lettering: C.H. Greenblatt. Coloring: Sno Cone Studios. "Left Out": Plot: Sam Henderson. Script, pencils, and inks: Jay Lender. Coloring: Digital Chameleon. Lettering: Sherm Cohen. "Best Fiend": Story, art, and lettering: C.H. Greenblatt. Coloring: Digital Chameleon. "Make that BigPants": Story: Walt Dohm, Art: Jay Lender, Lettering: Sherm Cohen, Coloring: Digital Chameleon. "Gone Jellyfishing": Story: Derek Drymon and Sherm Cohen. Pencils: Scott Roberts. Inks and lettering: Vince Deporter. Coloring: Digital Chameleon. "The Hole at the Bottom of the Sea": Story, art, and lettering: Sherm Cohen. Coloring: Digital Chameleon. "Dressed for Distress": Story, art, and lettering: C.H. Greenblatt. Coloring: Sno Cone Studios.

Special thanks to Stu Chaifetz. *Nick Magazine* SpongeBob comic staff: Andrew Brisman, Chris Duffy, Laura Galen, Tim Jones, Frank Pittarese, David Roman, Tina Strasberg, Catherine Tutrone, and Paul Tutrone. *Nick Magazine* would like to thank Stephen Hillenburg, Derek Drymon, and Sherm Cohen.

"PRIZE INSIDE"   7

"HICCUP! AND AWAY!"   9

"JUST DESSERTS"   19

"KRUSTY KRAB CLEANUP"   25

"DOLLARS AND SCENTS"   27

"LEFT OUT"   32

"BEST FIEND"   34

"MAKE THAT BIGPANTS"   43

"GONE JELLYFISHING"   45

"THE HOLE AT THE BOTTOM OF THE SEA"   53

"DRESSED FOR DISTRESS"   63

Yes!

My very own cereal bowl caddy!

Hang on, my new buddy, as I pour our cereal in...

...and add our milk!

Oh, this is going to be the best breakfast ever!

Pat! Pat!

DIG IN!

7

WE'VE GOT THE HOUSE SURROUNDED!!

Hello?...

HANDS UP!

NO FUNNY BUSINESS, SMALL-FINS McKLOWSKY!

Aww, nuts!

Thank you for your outstanding cooperation, citizen!

No problem.

What a way to start the day...

Whoa.

A getaway car!

end!

I'M READY!

HICCUP

HWROOOONK!

TIK TIK TIK TIK

NYA-HA, HA-HA! I'VE GOT THE HICCUPS!

WHAT A FUNNY WAY TO START MY DAY!

HIC

HMM... IT'S NOT QUITE AS FUNNY THE SECOND TIME.

9

GEE, THANKS, SQUIDWARD!

HEH, HEH... SUCKER!

HIC! CRASH HIC! BOOM HIC! BASH

HIC!

OH, NO! ≷SOB≷ LOOK WHAT YOU DID TO GLASSY!

I'M SORRY, SQUIDWARD, BUT YOUR IDEA DIDN'T WORK! HIC! DO YOU HAVE ANY OTHER IDEAS?

YES! GO BOTHER PATRICK!

HIC!

AND SO...

THE BEST THING TO DO IS TO STAND ON YOUR TONGUE AND HOLD YOUR BREATH.

LIGE YITH?

HIC!

AW, TARTAR SAUCE! I'LL NEVER GET RID OF THESE HICCUPS!

OH! YOU HAVE THE HICCUPS?

WELL, HIC! WHAT DID YOU THINK I SAID?

I THOUGHT YOU SAID YOU HAVE THE HICCUPS.

I DO HAVE THE HIC! HICCUPS!

OH, WELL, THE BEST THING TO DO IS TO STAND ON YOUR TONGUE...

NEVER MIND!

13

DID YOU STAND ON YOUR TONGUE?

YES!

DID YOU DUST SQUIDWARD'S SHELVES?

YES!

HOW ABOUT LAUNDRY DETERGENT?

YES! YES!

HICCUP!

I'VE TRIED THEM ALL!

WELL, IT LOOKS LIKE THERE'S ONLY ONE THING LEFT TO DO...

YOU'LL HAVE TO TAKE A TRIP TO...

HICCUP ISLAND

"HICCUP HICCUP! ISLAND"?

NO! NOT "HICCUP HICCUP ISLAND," JUST "HICCUP ISLAND."

LOOK HERE.

Isle of the Hiccups

HICCUP!

EVER SINCE PHLEGMY McWELTERSON CAUSED THE WRECK OF THE S.S. GLOTTIS, IT'S BEEN THE CUSTOM OF THE SEA TO BANISH ALL HICCUPPING SAILORS TO THIS ISLAND OF LOST SOULS.

BUT I'M NOT A SAILOR, MR. KRABS... I'M A FRY COOK!

AYE...THAT'S WHAT PHLEGMY McWELTERSON SAID, TOO.

C'MON, LAD...I'LL TAKE YOU THERE MYSELF.

IS THAT WHO I THINK IT IS?

AYE, IT'S THE FLYING DUTCHMAN.

BUT I THOUGHT HE LIVED IN DAVEY JONES'S LOCKER.

AHOY, KRABS! I SEE YOU BROUGHT ANOTHER LOST SOUL TO WALLOW HERE IN ETERNAL MISERY!

HIC!

YES, BUT HE SUMMERS HERE ON HICCUP ISLAND.

AYE, DUTCHMAN. HE BE AFFLICTED WITH THE HICCUPS!

DID HE TRY STANDING ON HIS--

YES, YES! HE DID ALL THAT.

WELL, IF YOU THINK THIS WRETCHED DOG HAS WHAT IT TAKES, LET'S HEAR HIM HICCUP!

GO ON, SPONGEBOB. HICCUP FOR THE FLYING DUTCHMAN.

...

WELL, I'M WAITING...

UMMM...OKAY. JUST A SECOND.

I'M A LITTLE BIT NERVOUS.

C'MON, LAD! YOU'RE MAKING ME LOOK BAD.

GULP! I'M SURE ONE'S COMING!

I HAVEN'T GOT ALL DAY! I WANT TO HEAR YOU HICCUP, AND I WANT TO HEAR IT *NOW!*

YES, A SUPER KOMBO MEAL, PLEASE.

CHEE P

ARE YOU CALLING ME CHEAP!?

YEAH, WELL, UNLIKE YOU RICH FAST-FOOD GUYS, I HAVE TO WORK HARD FOR MY MONEY BUYING AND SELLING STOCK!

YOU'RE JUST LUCKY MY BOYFRIEND ISN'T HERE OR HE'D POP YOU IN THE KISSER!

EXCUSE ME. PARDON ME. HEALTH INSPECTOR COMING THROUGH FOR A SURPRISE INSPECTION.

PLOP

SWEET MOTHER-OF-PEARL! THIS MAN HAS A HORRIBLE SKIN DISEASE!

YOU'RE ALL IN DANGER! RUN, YOU FOOLS! RUN AND PANIC!!

23

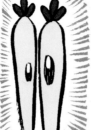

The End

"Krusty Krab Cleanup"

WE SHOULD TEST THE COLOGNE ON SQUID SINCE HE HAS THE BIGGEST NOSE!

AGREED!

THIS LOOKS LIKE A GOOD ONE.

CONFUSION
by Coral Clein

SQUIRT!

SNIFF SNIFF

KEEP TRYING.

IRRITATION
by Esteé Flounder

SQUIRT!

NOT YET.

SNIFF SNIFF

INFLAMMATION
by Shell Nell

SQUIRT! SQUIRT!

NOPE.

SNIFF

SQUIRT!
SQUIRT!
SQUIRT!
SQUIRT!

SQUIRT!
SQUIRT!
SQUIRT!
SQUIRT!

BOTTLE'S EMPTY. BETTER GET ANOTHER.

NO MORE!!

≡SIGH≡ WHERE ARE WE GONNA FIND THE PERFECT SCENT?

MAYBE UNDER THAT SIGN THAT SAYS "PERFECT SCENT."

29

THIS IS GOING TO DRIVE MRS. PUFF *WILD*!

STIR

ALL RIGHT! SCENT ME UP!

UHH... THIS STUFF IS PRETTY STRONG. WE SHOULD GO EASY.

NO WAY! I PAID FER ALL THEM INGREDIENTS! I WANT THE FULL TREATMENT!

BLOOSH!

OH, YEAH... I'M GETTIN' ME SOME SERIOUS KISSIE KISSIE TONIGHT!

DO YOU THINK HE'LL LIKE IT?

THE TENSION IS KILLING ME.

DING DONG!

COMING!

HELLO, EUGENE. HOPE YOU LIKE MY NEW PERFUME.

IT'S KRABBY PATTY SCENTED! WOW!

HAHA! I GUESS WE DIDN'T HAVE TO GO THROUGH ALL THAT AFTER ALL!

I HATE YOU SO MUCH.

DO I SMELL BABY PHOTOS AND SHOES? OH, EUGENE!

THE END

31

33

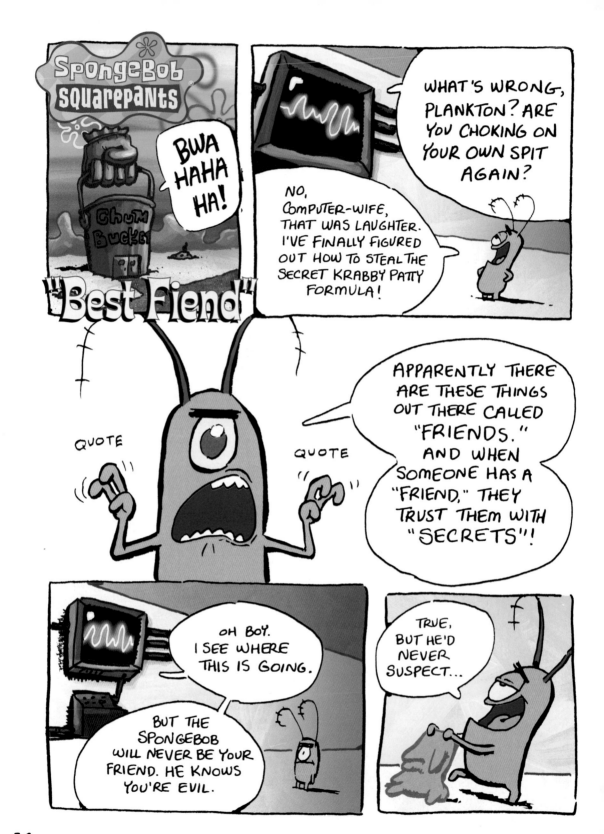

MOMENTS LATER...

OPEN UP! I COMMAND YOU TO OPEN THIS DOOR!

BINK BINK

BINK

WELL, A BIG HELLO TO--

AHEM!

OH! HEY, PATRICK!

YES, THAT'S RIGHT! I'M YOUR STUPID FRIEND, PATRICK!

BUT WE SHOULD BE OKAY. IT'S NOT AGGRESSIVE...

...TO ANYTHING BIGGER THAN A PLANKTON.

WOW! I'VE NEVER SEEN ONE THIS CLOSE!

ZAP

NEAT! THAT MUST BE THE VENOM SAC!

ZAP

I'VE READ THAT IT EVEN HAS STINGERS ON ITS STINGERS!

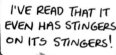

ZAP

HEY! NOW IT'S SLAPPING YOU! I DIDN'T KNOW IT COULD DO THAT!

ZAP

I THINK IT'S DONE. OH, WAIT...

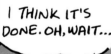

ZAP

NOW IT'S DONE.

THAT WAS INCREDIBLE, PATRICK!

AND SO...

YEP. WE'RE JUST TWO BEST FRIENDS, WALKING AND TALKING.

SAY, I'VE GOT A FUN IDEA FOR A GAME!

IT'S CALLED "LET'S TELL EACH OTHER SECRETS"! YOU GO FIRST! WHAT'S THE KRABBY PATTY FORMULA?

SORRY, PATRICK. WHAT WAS THAT? I WAS SINGING A SONG IN MY HEAD CALLED "SINGING LOUD."

WANNA HEAR IT?

NOT REALLY.

SINGING LOUD! SINGING LOUD! IF YOU MEAN IT, YOU GOTTA SCREAM IT! SINGING LOUD! SINGING LOUD! IF YOU MEAN IT, YOU GOTTA SCREAM IT!

BEEP!
BEEP!
BEEP!
BEEP!

HEY, PATRICK! YOU KNOW WHAT TIME IT IS?

TIME TO TALK ABOUT THE SECRET FORMULA?

NO, SILLY. IT'S TIME FOR OUR DAILY "JOGGING IN PLACE" DRILL!

GET THOSE KNEES UP HIGHER!

HIGHER! THIS COULD SAVE YOUR LIFE, PATRICK! YOU NEVER KNOW WHEN YOU'LL HAVE TO JOG IN PLACE IN AN EMERGENCY!

HIGHER! HIGHER!! HIGHER!!!

TWITCH!

TWITCH! TWITCH!

ALL RIGHT, THAT'S IT!!

ARE YOU OR ARE YOU NOT GOING TO TELL ME THE SECRET KRABBY PATTY FORMULA?!

THE SECRET FORMULA? WELL, OKAY.

IT'S REALLY SIMPLE. YOU JUST--

RUB RUB

HEY, SPONGEBOB!

WOW, LOOK! IT'S ME!

CURSE YOU ALL!

THAT WAS AWESOME, PATRICK! HOW'D YOU DO THAT?!

I'M JUST SPECIAL, I GUESS.

YOU SURE ARE, BUDDY. YOU SURE ARE.

I'M SMALLER IN PERSON THAN I WOULD'VE THOUGHT.

END!

45

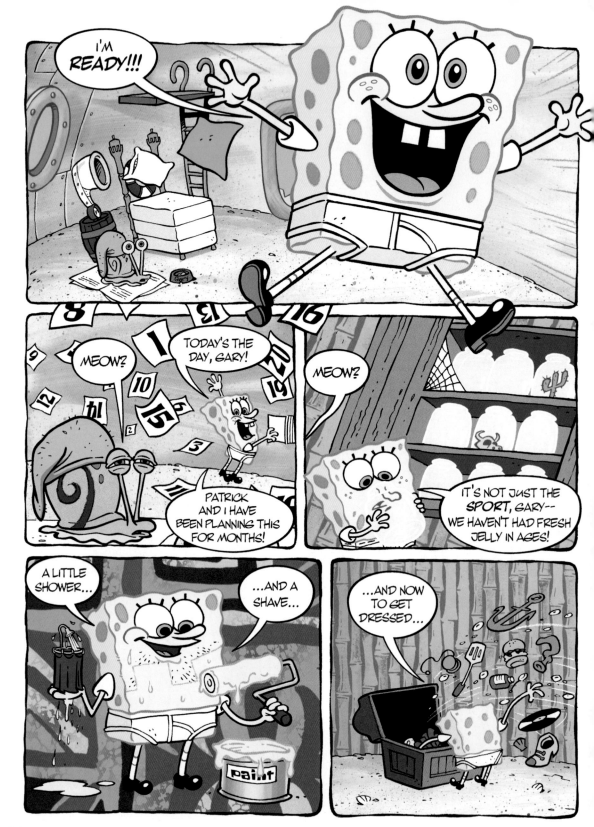

THIS IS THE COOLEST SPORT EVER!!!

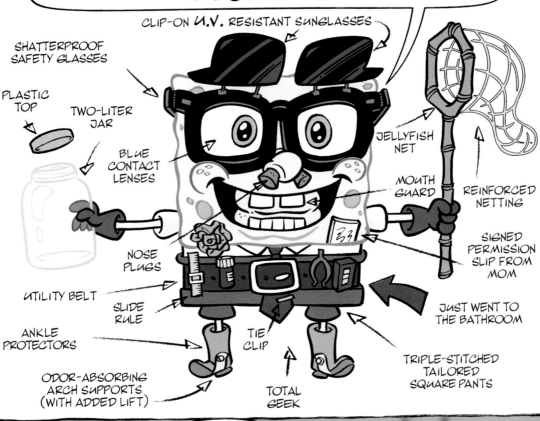

CLIP-ON **U.V.** RESISTANT SUNGLASSES

SHATTERPROOF SAFETY GLASSES

PLASTIC TOP

TWO-LITER JAR

BLUE CONTACT LENSES

JELLYFISH NET

MOUTH GUARD

REINFORCED NETTING

SIGNED PERMISSION SLIP FROM MOM

NOSE PLUGS

UTILITY BELT

SLIDE RULE

ANKLE PROTECTORS

ODOR-ABSORBING ARCH SUPPORTS (WITH ADDED LIFT)

TIE CLIP

TOTAL GEEK

JUST WENT TO THE BATHROOM

TRIPLE-STITCHED TAILORED SQUARE PANTS

WELL, I'D BETTER GET PATRICK!

HEY, PATRICK! READY TO GO?

NOK! NOK!

Z

HOW CAN YOU STILL BE SLEEPING ON THE MOST IMPORTANT DAY OF OUR LIVES?

ZZZ

AWW, WHO NEEDS HIM?

I CAN GO JELLYFISHING BY MYSELF!

WAIT! PATRICK AND I MADE A SOLEMN OATH LONG AGO...

GOO-GOO, GA-GA, BA-BLAH.

...AND THOSE WORDS STILL RING TRUE TODAY!

A B

I CAN'T LEAVE WITHOUT HIM!

C'MON, BUDDY, I WON'T LET YOU DOWN!

POP!

CRASH!

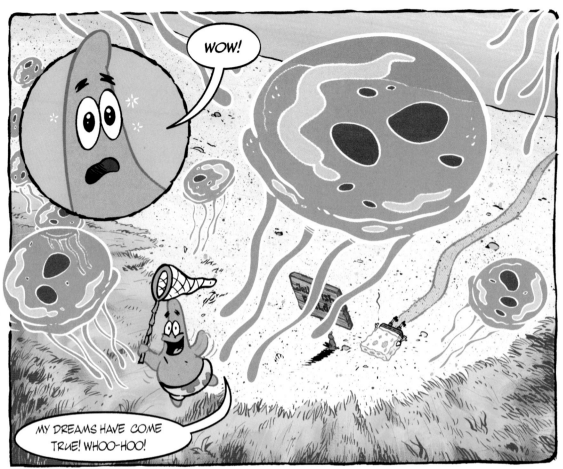

Hours later, night falls on Jellyfish Fields...

ZZZ--NIGHT?!

THAT MEANS I SLEPT THROUGH THE WHOLE DAY! I MISSED ALL THE JELLY!

I WONDER WHAT COULD HAVE HAPPENED TO...

...PATRICK!

WOW, SPONGEBOB--THAT WAS THE GREATEST DAY OF JELLYFISHING EVER! AND YOU SLEPT RIGHT THROUGH IT!

HOW COULD YOU GO JELLYFISHING WITHOUT ME? YOU DIDN'T EVEN SAVE ME ANY JELLY!

DON'T YOU REMEMBER WHAT GOO-GOO, GA-GA, BA-BLAH MEANS?

YEAH, IT MEANS "I JUST MESSED MY DIAPERS" IN BABY TALK. WE USED TO SAY IT ALL THE TIME.

OH...

...IS THAT WHAT IT MEANT?

END

WELL, SPONGEBOB... IN LIGHT OF YOUR YEARS OF OUTSTANDING SERVICE...

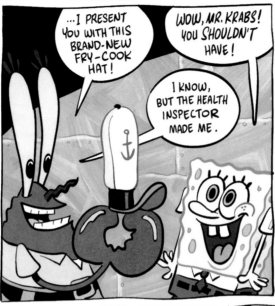

...I PRESENT YOU WITH THIS BRAND-NEW FRY-COOK HAT!

WOW, MR. KRABS! YOU SHOULDN'T HAVE!

I KNOW, BUT THE HEALTH INSPECTOR MADE ME.

SNIFF! IT'S BEAUTIFUL! I'LL NEVER WASH MY SCALP AGAIN!

LATER...

SEE YOU TOMORROW, MR. KRABS!

HOLD UP THERE, LAD! YOU FORGOT TO LEAVE YER UNIFORM BEHIND!

CLOSED

BUT... I WAS GONNA WEAR IT HOME WITH ME...

DON'T WORRY, BOY! IT'LL BE HERE WAITING FOR YE WHEN YOU COME IN TOMORROW!

BUT I PROMISE I'LL TAKE GOOD CARE OF IT...

BELAY THIS NONSENSE, BOY! THAT HAT DOESN'T PASS THROUGH THESE DOORS!

GULP! YES, MR. KRABS.

OF COURSE, HE DIDN'T SAY I COULDN'T TAKE IT OUT THROUGH *THIS DOOR*...

53

…SO, BACK AT THE BOTTOM…

NO ONE ROBS FROM OUR SACRED SHRINE AND LIVES!

HOW DARE YOU STEAL ONE OF THE GIFTS FROM ABOVE!

NOW, STRANGERS~ FEEL THE WRATH OF OUR KING!

BUT, YOUR HIGHNESS… THAT'S NOT A HOLY RELIC! IT'S JUST MY HAT THAT FELL DOWN THE HOLE!

I KNOW NOT THIS WORD "HAT" THAT YOU SPEAK…

…BUT THIS SURE MAKES A NIFTY COVER FOR MY FAVORITE GOLF CLUB! I'M AFRAID I CAN'T LET YOU HAVE IT!

WE NEED THAT HAT, OR WE'LL BE STUCK DOWN HERE FOREVER!

YOU GOT ANYTHING WE MIGHT BE ABLE TO TRADE HIM FOR IT?

ALL'S I GOT IS MY LUCKY YO-YO.

GREAT! I'LL BUY YOU A NEW ONE WHEN WE GET BACK!

WELL, YOUR HIGHNESS… WHY SETTLE FOR A SIMPLE GOLF-CLUB COVER WHEN YOU COULD TRADE IT FOR THIS SPLENDIFEROUS LUCKY YO-YO?

WHY, WITH THIS YO-YO, YOU CAN DO TRICKS LIKE THIS DOUBLE-INSIDE HOT-DOG FRENCH SWIRL! READY? WATCH!

THUD.

UH, NO THANKS…

…I'LL PASS.

WHY DO YOU CALL THAT YOUR "LUCKY" YO-YO?

'CAUSE I'M LUCKY IF I CAN GET IT TO *DO* ANYTHING!

NOW THERE'S ONLY ONE CHANCE LEFT... BUT I'VE *GOT TO TRY IT!*

AND SO...

SO LONG! GOOD LUCK!

TAKE CARE OF THAT NEW *CROWN!*

SNIFF! IT'S *BEAUTIFUL!* I'LL *NEVER* WASH MY SCALP AGAIN!

WELL, PATRICK... THAT WAS QUITE AN ADVENTURE... IT COST ME A GOOD PAIR OF UNDERPANTS, BUT I'M SURE GLAD WE MADE IT BACK HOME!

YIKES!

WE'RE GOING TOO HIGH!

DON'T WORRY--I'LL *POP* IT!

NO! PATRI--

60

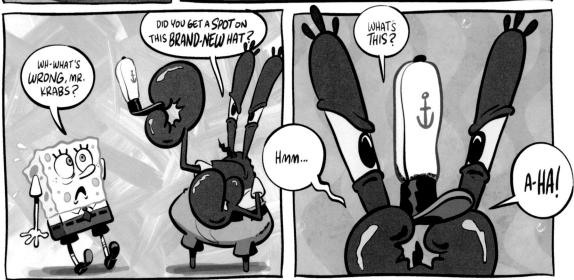

61

OH...IT WAS JUST A SHADOW. HERE YOU GO.

OK, YOU PASS INSPECTION!

TOK!

WHEW!

AAUGH! NO! MY HAT...

I'M SORRY, MR. KRABS!

AW, QUIT YER BLUBBERIN,' BOY!

THERE'S PLENTY MORE WHERE *THAT* CAME FROM!

OF COURSE, I'M GONNA TAKE IT OUT OF YER NEXT FEW PAY-CHECKS!

Oooohhh...

eno

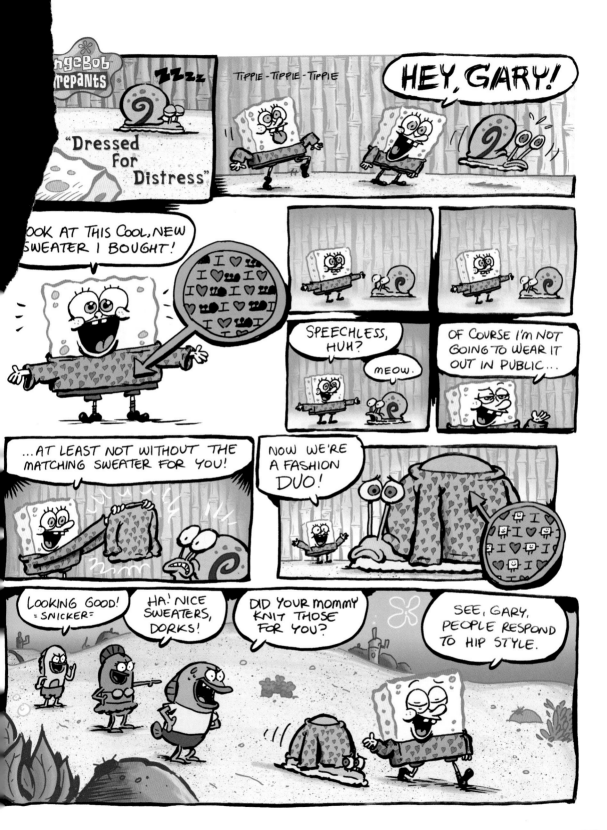

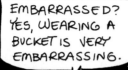

END